For all the girls, boys, moms & dads who have experienced the loss of family...this story of hope is for you. May you heal your hearts with patience, compassion, presence, insight, & above all LOVE.

TO GIA AND SIENNA
HUGS AND SMOOTCHES
KELLY

* This book is an intentional & creatively conscious collaboration, supporting local artists, utilizing sustainable FSC certified materials, endorsing a Canadian printer, & contributing to the North American economy. By purchasing this book, you are doing the same. Thank you. *

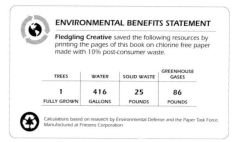

ENVIRONMENTAL BENEFITS STATEMENT

Fledgling Creative saved the following resources by printing the pages of this book on chlorine free paper made with 10% post-consumer waste.

TREES	WATER	SOLID WASTE	GREENHOUSE GASES
1	416	25	86
FULLY GROWN	GALLONS	POUNDS	POUNDS

Calculations based on research by Environmental Defense and the Paper Task Force. Manufactured at Friesens Corporation

Published by FLEDGLING CREATIVE
Founded in 2010
Calgary, Alberta, Canada.
www.fledglingcreative.com

Library and Archives Canada Cataloguing in Publication

Strumecki, Shannon, 1977-
    Pooka Monkers notices : a child's hopeful journey through family separation / story by Shannon Strumecki ; art by Kelly Sutherland.

ISBN 978-0-9868047-0-0

    I. Sutherland, Kelly, 1975- II. Title.

PS8637.T845P66 2011   jC813'.6   C2011-900269-8

Printed in Canada
Friesens Corporation
One Printers Way
Altona, MB. R0G 0B0

Graphic Design & Layout by Sara Swallow
www.saracreative.com

Pooka Monkers Notices

A Child's Hopeful Journey Through Family Separation

Story by Shannon Strumecki   Art by Kelly Sutherland

Pooka Monkers sits upon her bed - it's late at night,
Surrounded by Jack-Jack (stuffed cat) and a glowing star for light.

Her rainbow quilt and flower pillows soften up her bed,
Pooka Monkers sits with Mom and Dad thoughts in her head.

See, Pooka's five, but Mom and Dad divorced when she was four,
Pooka knows it's best 'cause they don't fight much anymore.

Pooka knows that Mom and Dad will always be close friends,
'Cause they share a little Pooka, and for her they make amends.

Pooka Monkers lives with Dad one week, and Mom the next,
Two separate homes, two separate Pooka rooms, two separate nests.

MOM'S HOUSE

ICE CREAM

ICE CREAM

BIG FENCE

CLIMBING TREE

PLAYGROUND

STINKY BOYS

RAINY PUDDLES

BAD DOG

HOPSCOTCH

DAD'S HOUSE

Pooka thinks it's neat to have two places she belongs,
But sometimes Pooka gets the blues and sings a saddened song.

"I understand my Mom and Dad need to live apart,
But sometimes I just want them both together in my heart."

Pooka hums softly so she doesn't wake her Dad,
She rests her head on Jack-Jack's chest, eyes heavy, little sad.

Pooka Monkers wakes up early, stretches to the sky,
She yawns aloud and stumbles to go see her favorite guy.

Her Dad is sleeping soundly in his big old Daddy bed,
Pooka climbs up quietly and kisses Daddy's head.

Daddy Monkers opens up one eye and smiles at her,
She's kind of like a kitty in the morning, stretch and purrr.

Pooka Monkers knows how much they love their morning snuggle,
They talk about the dreams they had, and giggle while they cuddle.

Pooka Monkers,
washed and ready,
waffles in her tum,

About to go to school,
can't help but have
thoughts of her Mum.

At first it's just a longing thought
of how much Mum is missed,

The Mum-tears shift to screams,
and its like Daddy don't exist.

"I MISS MY MOM! I MISS HER BAD!
I WANT HER HERE RIGHT NOW!"

Daddy does his best to wipe
    her tears and cheeks and brow.

"I know you miss your Momma Pook,
        it's normal to feel blue,
You'll see your Mom tomorrow,
        until then know I LOVE YOU."

But Pooka Monkers cries and cries
        and cries and cries and cries,
'Til she feels a little better
        and can wipe her puffy eyes.

Pooka in her car seat looks into the rear view mirror,

Miss Monkers sees her Daddy's reassuring smile appear.

Tomorrow comes and Pooka will go spend time with her Mom,
Living at her second house she'll know that she belongs.

Often during weeks with Mom she'll think about her Dad,
She'll sing her missing Daddy song, and sometimes she'll feel sad.

Moms are good at snuggles, smooches, hugs and kisses too,
But when Pooka misses Daddy, there's not much Mom can do.
So Mom just sits there patiently, and lovingly she knows,
That Pooka will learn lots by having feelings as she grows.

The next few months go
by and Pooka Monkers
plays a lot,

She colors, swims,
and rides her bike,
and wipes away her snot.

Pooka gives
Jack-Jack a voice,
and plays pretend outside,

She dances, sings,
and skateboards, and
sometimes plays Seek and Hide.

The Monkers parents NOTICE Pooka isn't sad as much,
They chat about how happy Pooka Monkers seems and such.

They talk about how Pooka Monkers still has lots of feelings,
But how Pooka seems to have grown up in how she handles dealings.

Mom and Dad show up to Pooka's school one afternoon,
It's Family Day, and kids show parents what they've done 'til June.

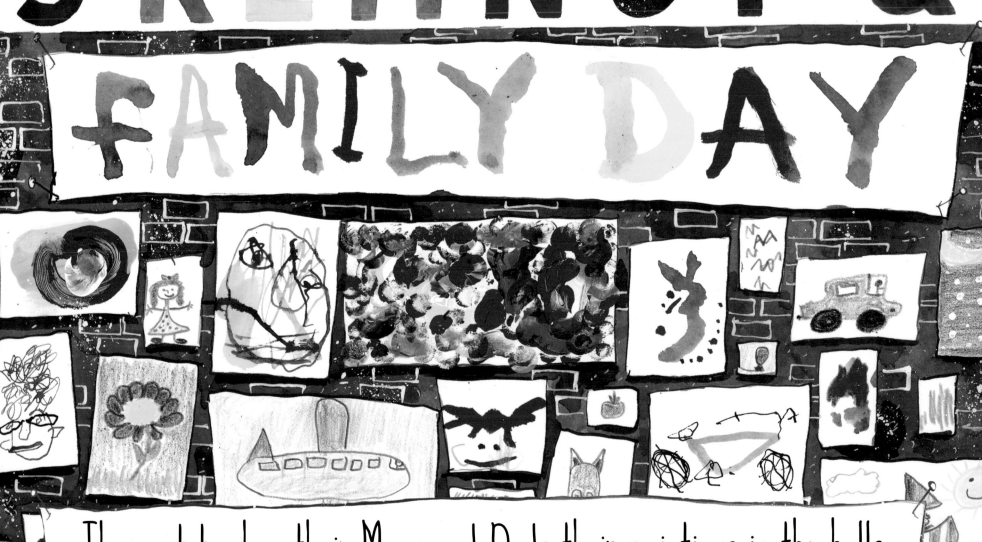

They get to show their Moms and Dads their paintings in the halls,
Families celebrate the year of school and kick 'round balls.

Dad and Mom are talking to
Miss Pooka Monker's teacher,

She raves 'bout Pooka's qualities...
"she's such a delightful creature!"

Then Mom and Dad turn heads to notice Pooka with her buddy,
She sits beside her friend Ben, he is sad and a little muddy.

Mom and Dad approach,
but stop a few feet away,

They give Pook her privacy,
and so they stay at bay.

Ben is telling Pooka that his Dad and Mom split up,
Ben asks if Pooka knows what that feels like, and she says "yup"

Ben begins to sob; Pook puts her arm around his waist,
She tells him 'bout her Mom and Dad, and all that she has faced.

Pooka tells him that she used to cry and scream and kick,
Until she saw that NOTICING might do the trick.

"What do you mean by NOTICING?" Ben asked as he stopped crying.
Pooka explained that she started to NOTICE how much her parents were trying.

"When I was crying for Mom I couldn't NOTICE that I was with Dad.
When I wanted for something that wasn't right there, I didn't NOTICE what I had."

"When you miss your Mom, just give her a call to hear her voice,
Or better yet, just NOTICE your Dad is there - you have a choice."

"And when you miss your Dad, just tell your Mom what you are feeling,
Then NOTICE your Mom there loving you...your broken heart is healing."

Ben hugged Pooka, then he ran to climb and swing and play,
Pooka's teacher lovingly watched her students enjoy the day.

Mom and Dad made a Pooka sandwich and looked into her eyes,
They couldn't have been more proud of Pooka Monkers,

for she was wise.

Shannon Strumecki is a multi-talented artist, joyfully working & playing in Calgary, Alberta, Canada. For their unwavering love & support, Shannon's heartfelt gratitude is extended to her parents, Bill & Maureen. Shannon's deepest admiration & respect to the incomparable Kelly Sutherland, whose genius co-created a magical world where Pooka & this process could grow. To Sara Swallow, who painstakingly nurtured Pooka's story with the most detailed integration of art & design & word. Thank you Emma, Heather.H, Jody, Andrew, Makenna, Kaelen, Maureen.O, Lara, Wendy, Warren, Ken, Clare, Chris, Rebekah, the McEwans, & Shannon's unconditionally loving partner Mark. Hugs & kisses to friends & family who took the time to encourage this project.
You know who you are.
Shannon continues to inspire & ignite a career & life built on childhood dreams.
Dare to live your BIGGEST life.
www.fledglingcreative.com
www.pookamonkers.com
www.shannonstrumecki.com

Kelly Sutherland has illustrated for numerous magazines all over North America. Originally from Saskatchewan, he now calls Calgary, Alberta his home. When not sketching & painting, Kelly can be found writing & playing original music as the lead singer of Seven Story Redhead. Kelly whiles away his time creating a unique brand of kooky art with his fabulous wife Heather and their two cats: Zoe and Solomon.
To see more of Kelly's work visit **www.el-freako.com**.